Get ready for a reading adventure with

Here's how...

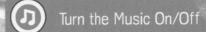

D1172127

Read the Page

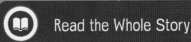
Read the Whole Story →

Repeat

Stop

Play Word Hunt →

Play a Game

Turn the Music On/Off

"¡Hola! Today Abuela is helping us make a Seasons Scrapbook," said Dora.

"We need to take pictures of the different seasons," said Dora.

"Will you help us?" asked Dora.
"¡Excelente! Come on! ¡Vámonos!"

picture frame

Summer

Spring

Fall

Winter

"Where should we go first, Dora?" asked Boots.

"Let's look at Map," said Dora. "Spring, Summer, Fall, and then Winter!"

"So first, we go to Spring Garden! Come on! ¡Vámonos! Let's go!" said Dora.

"So we can take pictures for the Seasons Scrapbook!" said Boots.

bridge

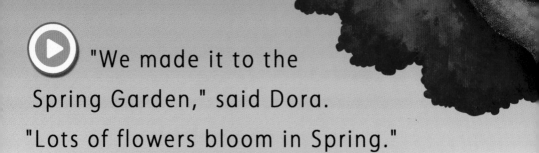

"We made it to the Spring Garden," said Dora. "Lots of flowers bloom in Spring."

"Wow! There are so many flowers!" said Boots.

 "Let's take some Spring pictures of them for the Seasons Scrapbook," said Dora. "Ready? Smile, flowers!"

"We made it to Summer Beach," said Dora. "We can swim and make sand castles!"

"I love summer, I love summer!" said Boots.

beach ball

pail

seashell

crab

"Boots, will you take a picture of me for our Seasons Scrapbook?" asked Dora.

"Of course Dora! Smile!" said Boots.

umbrella

sand castle

"Look at all the leaves on the ground, Dora! We must have made it to Fall!" said Boots.

"¡Sí! We made it to the Fall Forest," said Dora. "Let's take some pictures!"

snowman

"We made it to the last season, Winter! ¡El invierno!" said Dora.

"Look at all the snow, Dora," said Boots.

"Let's make some snowmen!"

 "Great idea, Boots. And then we can take some pictures of them!" said Dora.

"It looks like it's going to snow even more tonight," said Boots. "Look at those clouds!"

"Those clouds look like numbers," said Dora. "Let's count the number snow clouds!"

chimney

"Wow, Dora! We took so many pictures!" said Boots.

"Now we can put them in our Seasons Scrapbook!" said Dora.

"We did it! Yay!" said Dora and Boots.

-The End-

Dora's living room

sofa